About this Book

Meet Benji. His family just moved into a new town and he has started the year in a new school. He is nervous at first, but learns that he has all the tools to meet each new day and challenge, head on. Even when life changes again in the spring, Benji still figures out what to do to keep his cool. Basically, the character, Benji in this this book could be any student who has been (or started) in school before, and/or during the COVID pandemic. This is a story of hope and of family and a reminder to ALL children that: You are not alone in this unique and sometimes difficult time in our history.

This book is dedicated to my wonderful sons, Benji, Jonny and Raphael and to my loving husband, Shai.

WHAT IF
THIS IS THE BEST YEAR
EVER?

After I finished 1st grade, my family decided to travel around the world and drive throughout the United States. It was so much fun to see all kinds of different places as we drove ALL across the country in an RV. An RV is like a little house on wheels. We went to National Parks. We saw rivers, oceans and lakes.

We visited my grandparents. We met new people and we visited friends we hadn't seen in a long time. Best of all, we brought our home with us the whole time and we had lots of family time.

At the end of our year of adventures and homeschooling in the RV, we all wanted to go back to school. However, instead of going back to where we used to live, my parents chose a place to live in California.

We parked our RV outside our new apartment and moved in.

It was so exciting to have a room again after living in a small space all year. Even so, the first night in a new place can be a little scary. I was happy about my new bed and my new room, but I still wanted to snuggle longer with Mom that first night. Like every night since I was a baby, she read to me and rubbed my back until I fell asleep.

That night I had a dream about my old school. I was in my old classroom with my friends and I was telling them about my trip. In my dream, I was showing them a map of the world, like the one in my room, and I was pointing to all the places I had been.

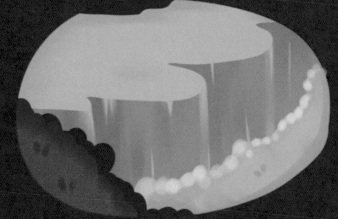

My heart felt a bit achy when I woke up and remembered that I was going to a start at a new school where I didn't know my way around or have friends yet. I gave myself a hug to feel better.

SCHOOL SUPPLIES

I went shopping with my mom to get ready for my first day of school.

My mom said I would be a student at the very same school she went to as a child.

She was really excited for me and my brothers to be students there too. We bought some new school supplies and I got a treat afterwards for being so helpful.

I was nervous on that first morning of school. Everything was new and a welcome buddy showed me to my class so I wouldn't get lost. I saw the teacher's name outside and placed my backpack on a hook. I squeezed my favorite rock inside my pocket to give me courage and I walked in to find a seat.

I had this butterfly feeling in my belly as I got ready to introduce myself to the class for the first time. I took a deep breath and closed my eyes to decide what I wanted to say before saying it outloud. That calmed me down and gave me confidence to speak.

Hello my name is Benjamin, but my friends call me Benji

Things went better than I had imagined. My new class and teacher were really nice and happy to meet me.

During recess, I saw that all the games were different than the ones I used to play at my old school. I sat down on the "friendship bench", which my teacher had explained was a place to sit when looking for someone to play with.

Some kids were playing four-square and invited me to join in. They taught me how to play. I could tell that I would get good at the new games and liked my new friends.

At lunchtime, everyone sat outside on the picnic benches. My welcome buddy sat with me and we ate from our lunch boxes as he told me about our school and about some of the fun things to do in my new neighborhood.

After lunch, we had music class. It was so much fun! Everyone got an instrument and we pretended to be a band, performing on stage. After music, we had P.E. and got to swim in the swimming pool.

By the end of the day, I was having so much fun that I didn't want to go home

When my mom came to pick me up, I saw that there were a lot of children and parents on the playground staying after school to play. My mom let me play on the playground while she talked to some of the other moms. My brothers were happy to stay too. My mom said she even saw people who she used to go to this school with.

One of the best things about moving to my mom's hometown was being able to have Grandpa and Grandma visit more often. Grandpa came to stay with us over Thanksgiving and we all had such a fun time going to all the places he used to take my mom to play when she was little.

The school year was flying by. I had made some great new friends and had gotten really good at the recess games. There were birthday parties and playdates and after school classes that I loved. My new school was feeling fun and familiar. Everything was great. Then, one day in March, my mom got a strange text at her parent-teacher conference. School was cancelled the next day for safety.

The next day, Mom got an email from school saying that they would be closed for two weeks because people were getting sick and that everyone needed to stay home to be safe.

21 My mom and I went shopping together to make sure we had lots of yummy food in the house. The shelves were a bit empty and there were many things missing already.

My mom looked worried, so I gave her a smile and told her that we would find everything we needed, and we did.

CEREAL

The next time we went to the store, we had to wear face masks. There were even more things missing, but we always found what we actually needed.

ONE WAY

Please WAIT HERE

Time passed slowly for the rest of the spring because I couldn't see my friends and school was closed. My mom and dad helped my brothers and I with our school work and we saw our teachers and classmates on the computer a few times each week. We had to stay home a long time, so we found a lot of things to do at home. We took long walks and admired the wildflowers. And, we got more hugs and cuddles from Mom and Dad.

Just after school ended, we were allowed to go to the park again. I got to see one friend from my class. We were so happy to see each other again that the distance and the masks didn't bother us. We still had a fun summer even though things had changed so much and we all looked different.

Right before the new school year was about to start, Mom got another email. I would be starting school online with video, not in person, like before. I wondered who would be in my class and if I would have any of my new friends with me. To be honest, I was nervous about what school would be like. My mom reminded me that, like every other year, I would be just fine and would make friends. Whenever I got nervous, I counted to ten and took deep breaths to calm the butterfly feeling in my stomach.

Today I am helping my mom to get everything ready for school. We put a desk and chair in my bedroom and set up my brothers' desks in the living room. School starts tomorrow and I am excited and nervous to meet my new teacher. She left my new computer and folders for me in the gym.

It's almost my turn to say hello to the class. What am I going to say? I make sure to turn on my camera and unmute myself before I speak. My mom gives me a big smile from the doorway, I sit up tall and now I feel ready to start.

Hi, my name is Benjamin, but my friends call me Benji

I still really like to play at recess. There is a new game my friends at school have taught me and I am getting really good at it.

Recess

10:00

75%

It's time for lunch and I am hungry from all the thinking in school. I wonder what is for lunch today. I walk into the kitchen and eat with my mom and brothers.

Lunch is over. This afternoon,
I have music and P.E. classes before
school finishes.. I bring out my
recorder and play with the class.
The music sounds funny, but we
are still having so much fun.
During P.E. I practice somersaults,
on the carpet.

Phew, my first day of school is over and I had fun. We get right out of the house. Time to go play outside. My mom says getting some exercise is just what I need after a long first day of school online. I tell my mom all about my teacher and new friends at the park.

Even though the play structure is still closed, we love to play frisbee on the grass.

CAUTION CAUTION CAUTION CAUTION

PARK
CLOSED

CAUTION CAUTION CAUTION CAUTION

CAUTION CAUTION CAUTION CAUTION

CAUTION CAUTION CAUTION CAUTION

Although the play structures
were still closed, we still liked
to play frisbee on the grass.

Back at home, it's time to help get everything ready for dinner. First, we wash our hands, then my brothers and I help Mom cook. I really like to peel the vegetables, my brother cleans and sets the table.

Twinkle, twinkle, little star
How I wonder what you are..

SURPRISE, Grandma and Grandpa visit us for dinner. They visit us even more now than before.

Today wasn't so scary after all. Everything was new, but it was new for everyone, even my teacher. My new teacher is nice and now I know some of the kids in my class. I wonder what tomorrow will be like. I take some deep breaths and count backwards from ten until I feel calm and relaxed. I snuggle closer to Dad and listen to a story before I go to sleep. Whatever happens tomorrow, I know that I will be just fine!

At night, I dream about what school might look like tomorrow and I know that I will do my best no matter how school looks.

About the Author

This is the first children's book written by Mira Celeste Nissim. She is a Montessori educator, world traveler, yogini, and the mother of three wonderful boys. In the midst of the global pandemic, she decided to write this book in order to show children that they are not alone in all the uncertainties and changes of 2020. She lives in California, on the Monterey Peninsula, with her husband and their sons where they are patiently awaiting the return of school in person, actively navigating a virtual lifestyle and enjoying the nature of their local area.

To see more from Mira Nissim, visit YouTube and Instagram @MiraTheMontessorian;
FaceBook Page: @MontessoriEssentials
email: montessoriessentials@gmail.com

About the Illustrators

The illustrations in this book were described by Mira and made by Kanare, a creative agency located in Lombok, Indonesia. The illustrators can be found on fiverr.com as @inamirna, on Instagram as @kanare.id or by email at kanaredesignco@gmail.com

What If This Was the Best Year Ever?

Written by Mira Celeste Nissim
Illustrations were imagined by Mira Celeste Nissim
and created by Kanare

First Published through Kindle Direct Publishing in 2021

Copyright belongs to Mira Celeste Nissim 2021

Made in the USA
Middletown, DE
06 June 2021